Charles Peattie and Mark Warren

Masterley Publishing

Celeb

First published in 2002 by
MASTERLEY PUBLISHING

Design and digital artwork by
OCEAN Digital Media.com

These cartoons first appeared in Private Eye between 1987 and 2002

With thanks to:

Ian Hislop for first "discovering" Gary,
Russell Taylor for additional material,
and Harry Enfield for being a great Bloke.

HERE, LISTEN TO THIS:— "ANOTHER CELEBRITY CLIENT, GARY BLOKE, WAS SEEN ENTERING THE EXCLUSIVE MASSAGE CLUB, MIDDAY ON TUESDAY..."

"...HE LEFT 15 MINUTES LATER BY THE FRONT DOOR. HIS CAR BRAZENLY PARKED OUTSIDE..." BLOODY LIARS!

THEY MAKE IT UP AS THEY GO ALONG. I FIND IT VERY HURTFUL.

I WAS IN THERE FOR A GOOD HOUR AND A HALF. CHANTELLE WAS QUITE EXHAUSTED.

BASTARDS!

BELUGA CAVIARE? NO THANKS MATE.

YOU SURE?

POSITIVE. I USED TO QUITE LIKE IT, AS IT HAPPENS, BUT THEN I FOUND OUT WHERE IT COMES FROM.

WHAT, RUSSIA?

NAH. FISHES' BOTTOMS.

ONLY JOKING. GISSA DOLLOP.

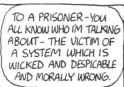

I KNOW I'M NOT SUPPOSED TO SAY ANYTHING POLITICAL BUT I JUST WANT TO SEND THIS MESSAGE OF GOODWILL...

TO A PRISONER—YOU ALL KNOW WHO I'M TALKING ABOUT— THE VICTIM OF A SYSTEM WHICH IS WICKED AND DESPICABLE AND MORALLY WRONG.

THEY'VE LOCKED HIM AWAY. THEY'VE TAKEN AWAY HIS LIBERTY... AND NOW THEY'VE TAKEN AWAY THE ONE THING HE VALUES ABOVE ALL ELSE...

HIS O.B.E.

LESTER PIGGOT. HERE'S TO YOU MATE. VICTIM OF THE MOST VICIOUS AND DRACONIAN TAXATION SYSTEM THE WORLD HAS EVER...

ER...

MY BIRTHDAY PARTY AT STRINGFELLOWS? SMASHING LITTLE BASH THAT WAS. BEST EVER.

NOTHING TOO GLITZY MIND. NONE OF THIS SHOWGIRLS JUMPING OUT OF CAKES MALARKEY I THINK THAT'S PONCEY.

NOT YOUR STYLE, GARY.

NAH. YOU'LL NEVER GUESS WHAT PETER LAID ON INSTEAD.

WHAT?

HE HAD THEM JUMP OUT FROM THIS IMMENSE SHEPHERDS PIE. THREE OF THEM THERE WAS. SISTERS.

OH THAT'S NICE

VERY TASTY.

Panel 1: HERE. GUESS WHAT? SUSSEX UNIVERSITY ARE AWARDING ME AN HONORARY DOCTORATE.
REALLY? WHAT IN?

Panel 2: ER... A SCARLET GOWN TRIMMED WITH AQUAMARINE LAPELS... A WHITE BOW TIE...

Panel 3: AND A FUNNY SORT OF OLD-FASHIONED FLOPPY HAT...
NAH, I MEAN WHAT SUBJECT?

Panel 4: ER... P.H.D. IN MUSICOLOGY I THINK.
WOW THAT SOUNDS PRETTY ACADEMIC.

Panel 5: TOTALLY ACADEMIC IN MY CASE, BARRY. I CAN'T EVEN SPELL IT.
YOU LAD.

Panel 1: I SUPPOSE YOU'VE HEARD THE LATEST ABOUT THE BIMBO DIARIES?
NO.

Panel 2: THE LITTLE FLOOZIE'S SPREADING RUMOURS ABOUT ME NOW. SAYS WE ENGAGED IN CARNAL ACTIVITIES ON SEVERAL OCCASIONS AND SHE CLAIMS THAT I USED A CERTAIN WHITE SUBSTANCE...

Panel 3: IS IT TRUE?
COURSE IT IS.

Panel 4: I TIPPEXED OUT ALL THE BITS ABOUT ME WHILE SHE WAS ASLEEP ONCE.

Panel 1: I GET VERY CHOKED WHEN I THINK OF THE WAY THE MEDIA HAVE TREATED JOHN LENNON, BARRY. I FEEL QUITE PERSONALLY AGGRIEVED...

Panel 2: JUST BECAUSE THE BLOKE HAPPENED TO BE ONE OF THE BEATLES, DOES IT MEAN HIS WHOLE PRIVATE LIFE HAS TO BE OPEN TO PUBLIC SCRUTINY?

Panel 3: I DO NOT SEE WHY WHAT THAT MAN DID IN BED IS HELD IN SUCH MORBID FASCINATION BY THE PRESS.
POK POK

Panel 4: YOU'RE STILL UPSET ABOUT THEM PAYING NO ATTENTION TO YOUR OWN "LIE-IN FOR PEACE" BACK IN 1969, AREN'T YOU, GARY?
COULD HAVE BEEN FRONT PAGE NEWS BUT FOR JOHN AND YOKO'S COPY-CAT STUNT THE PREVIOUS WEEK.

Panel 1: OH DEAR. I BET YOU'RE REGRETTING RUNNING INTO MIKE TYSON IN THAT NEW YORK NIGHTCLUB LAST WEEK, GARY.
INDEED, BARRY.

Panel 2: BUT I'LL TELL YOU... I'M PROUD I HAD A GO. EVEN THOUGH I DID KNOW HE'S HEAVYWEIGHT CHAMPION OF THE WORLD...

Panel 3: BESIDES, AFTER THE THINGS HE SAID TO ME THERE WAS NO WAY I COULD BACK DOWN. YOU KNOW WHAT HE CALLED ME?

Panel 4: A GENIUS. SAID HE HAD ALL MY RECORDS AND EVERYTHING...
WELL I STILL WOULDN'T HAVE RISKED SHAKING HANDS WITH HIM...

OFF LICENCE

'ELLO ARTHUR, I WANT A COUPLE OF CASES OF SOMETHING REALLY SPECIAL AS A CHRISTENING PRESENT.

CERTAINLY MR BLOKE SIR. DID YOU HAVE ANYTHING PARTICULAR IN MIND?

NOT REALLY NO. RECOMMEND SOMETHING.

WELL A GOOD VINTAGE PORT IS A POPULAR GIFT ON OCCASIONS SUCH AS THIS.

YEAH ALRIGHT. WHAT'S THE BEST YEAR TO BUY THEN?

IT ALL DEPENDS... PRESUMABLY YOU'D LIKE SOMETHING FOR LAYING DOWN NOW....

NAH. FALLING OVER ON SUNDAY MORE LIKE.

CERTAINLY SIR.

I THINK A LOT OF YOU KNOW ABOUT THE INVOLVEMENT THAT STING, PETE GABRIEL AND I HAVE WITH THE ISSUE OF BASIC HUMAN RIGHTS...

OUR DREAM FOR 1989 IS TO SEE A WORLD WITHOUT LOCKS AND CHAINS, WITHOUT BARRED WINDOWS AND BARBED-WIRE FENCES...

A WORLD IN WHICH WE CAN LIVE, NEVER KNOWING THE HOWL OF THE SIREN OR THE GRIM TREAD OF THE SENTRY'S BOOT...

THIS CHRISTMAS I WANT YOU ALL TO SPARE A THOUGHT FOR THE PEOPLE WHO HAVE TO LIVE WITH THESE CONDITIONS EVERY HOUR OF THE DAY...

PEOPLE LIKE MYSELF: PREMIER ENTERTAINERS, TO WHOM PERSONAL SECURITY AND BASIC PRIVACY, WITHOUT THESE MEASURES WOULD BE ABSOLUTELY IMPOSSIBLE AND...

CUT.

COR...LAST NIGHT... WAS I OUT OF ORDER OR WHAT?

SIR DOESN'T REMEMBER?

OH NO... WHAT WAS I DOING? BEING OFFENSIVE TO STRANGE BIRDS? CRACKING LEWD JOKES? TALKING RUBBISH AND BEHAVING LIKE A RIGHT WALLY?

ALL OF THOSE THINGS, SIR.

BLIMEY. GOD KNOWS WHAT I WAS ON.

CELEBRITY SQUARES CHRISTMAS SPECIAL I BELIEVE, SIR.

OH YEAH THAT'S RIGHT.

YOU KNOW, I WAS TOTALLY PISSED ALL THE WAY THROUGH IT.

IT DIDN'T SHOW, SIR.

NEW BOOK, GARY?

YEP.

WHAT'S IT ABOUT, THEN?

IT'S A SEARING INDICTMENT OF THE SUPERFICIALITY AND HYPOCRISY OF LIFE IN THE LATE 80'S... A PATHETIC CATALOGUE OF DOUBLE STANDARDS AMONG THE RICH AND FAMOUS.

COR.

WHAT THEY GET UP TO IN PUBLIC AND IN PRIVATE AND HOW POWER AND INFLUENCE IN THE WRONG HANDS RUTHLESSLY SETS OUT TO STAMP ON TALENT.

NEW JACKIE COLLINS?

NAH. THE NEW WHO'S WHO. BASTARDS HAVE LEFT ME OUT.

I'VE FOUND LORD LUCAN.

LORD WHO?

THE DOCTORS ON EARTH ARE SAYING THAT IF I DON'T SHOW SIGNS OF RECOVERY SOON THERE'LL BE NO ALTERNATIVE BUT FOR THEM TO SWITCH OFF MY LIFE SUPPORT MACHINE.

BASTARDS. I'VE A GOOD MIND TO TALK TO GOD ABOUT THIS. WHO DO THEY THINK THEY ARE?

ISN'T MY LIFE IMPORTANT? IT'S DIABOLICAL, ANGEL. THEY CAN'T DO THIS TO ME, SURELY?

I MEAN, WHY CAN'T THEY GET KYLIE MINOGUE TO DO THE HONOURS? SHE DID THE OXFORD ST. LIGHTS LAST XMAS.

I THINK YOU'LL FIND SHE'S BUSY.

WHERE AM I? WHERE AM I?

IT'S OKAY, MR BLOKE. YOU'RE IN HOSPITAL.

WHAT'S GOING ON? EVERYTHING'S A BLANK.

YOU'VE BEEN UNCONSCIOUS BUT YOU'RE QUITE SAFE NOW. RELAX.

WHEN DID I PASS OUT THEN? WHO ARE YOU ANYWAY?

I'M A NURSE. NOW CALM DOWN. EVERYTHING'S ALRIGHT.

I BLOODY WELL HOPE SO. LAST TIME THIS HAPPENED I FOUND OUT I'D GOT MARRIED.

ABOUT GARY: IS HE ALL RIGHT?

HE'S FINE NOW. RIGHT BACK TO HIS NORMAL SELF, BLESS HIM.

HE'S STILL IN BED THOUGH?

OH YEAH. HE'LL HAVE TO REMAIN THERE FOR A FEW DAYS, I EXPECT.

BUT HE'S NOT IN A COMA ANY MORE?

NO. HE'S TOTALLY OUT OF IT.

OH I SEE.

FIRST THING HE ASKED FOR WHEN HE WOKE UP.

OF COURSE I'M WORRIED ABOUT THE ATMOSPHERE. YOU'VE GOT TO BE IN THIS DAY AND AGE.

LET'S FACE FACTS. WE'VE BEEN PUMPING TONS OF CARBON DIOXIDE INTO IT FOR YEARS NOW. IT CAN'T GO ON LIKE THIS SURELY?

SOMETHING MUST CHANGE. I'D LIKE TO SEE A RADICAL RETHINK ON HOW WE USE OUR RESOURCES. THAT'S NOT TOO MUCH TO ASK IS IT?

I MEAN, WE'VE HAD DRY ICE AT MY GIGS SINCE THE SEVENTIES, GAVIN. TALK ABOUT PASSÉ...

I'M ONLY GIVING YOUR PUBLIC WHAT THEY WANT, SUGAR.

25

THE PROSECUTION IN YOUR MANSLAUGHTER CASE ARE GOING TO DO THEIR UTMOST TO DEPICT YOU AS SOME SORT OF DEBAUCHED VIOLENT MONSTER.

AS YOUR LAWYER I SUGGEST WE COMBAT THIS BY ASKING A CELEBRITY FRIEND OF YOURS TO APPEAR IN COURT AS A CHARACTER REFERENCE.

SOMEONE WHO WILL MAKE THE JURY SEE THAT YOU'RE NOT REALLY THE ULTIMATE OGRE AND EPITOME OF DEPRAVITY AFTER ALL. I KNOW JUST THE MAN.

OLIVER REED?

YEAH. HE'LL MAKE ME LOOK LIKE AN ANGEL WON'T HE?

I SHALL NOW PLAY THE SONG WHICH I BELIEVE CAUSED A TEENAGE FAN TO LEAP FROM HIS BEDROOM WINDOW TO HIS DEATH.

THE SATANIC LYRICS, REFERENCE TO RITUAL SLAUGHTER AND CHORUS "DO IT NOW DIE" DERANGED HIS MIND, WITH TRAGIC RESULTS.

YOU'RE MY LAWYER, DAVID. DON'T JUST SIT THERE. DO SOMETHING.

TAP YOUR FEET...CLICK YOUR FINGERS...AT LEAST PRETEND YOU LIKE IT.

THE PUBLICITY SURROUNDING GARY'S COURT CASE HAS KNOCKED HIM FOR SIX. I'VE NEVER KNOWN HIM SO DEPRESSED.

WELL HE HASN'T EXACTLY BEEN DEPICTED WELL IN COURT BY THE PRESS HAS HE?

NO. HE'S ABSOLUTELY DEVASTATED...I'M REALLY WORRIED ABOUT HIM.

I SAW HIS PICTURE IN YESTERDAY'S PAPER. HE LOOKED AWFUL. GAUNT, HAGGARD, DREADFULLY DRAWN...

I KNOW.

PATHETICALLY DRAWN. YOU CAN'T EVEN TELL IT'S ME.

COURTROOM ARTISTS. WHERE DO THEY GET THEM?

I'VE HEARD THE PIECE OF MUSIC WHICH IS ALLEGED TO HAVE LED TO THE DEATH OF A YOUNG MAN...

AND I HAVE TO SAY THAT I WAS SHOCKED BY THE LYRICAL CONTENT AND SENTIMENTS EXPRESSED

MERE WORDS CAN HARDLY DESCRIBE MY FEELINGS ABOUT THIS SONG. IT'S... WELL, IT'S... WELL, WICKED.

WELL WICKED EH? NICE ONE. THINGS ARE LOOKING UP AT LAST.

IN MY PREVIOUS MARRIAGES I ALWAYS GOT BORED AFTER A COUPLE OF YEARS. THE PHYSICAL ATTRACTION WANED AND I'D RUN OFF WITH A DIFFERENT WOMAN.

IT DOESN'T HAVE TO BE LIKE THAT WITH US THOUGH DOLL . I'M MORE MATURE AND SENSIBLE NOW. I STILL FIND YOU ATTRACTIVE, DON'T GET ME WRONG...

BUT FOR ME, A SUCCESSFUL RELATIONSHIP IS WHERE TWO PEOPLE CAN LIVE HAPPILY TOGETHER...CHANGING AND ADAPTING AS THEY GROW OLDER...

WHAT EXALTLY ARE YOU TRYING TO SAY, GARY?

I'LL HAVE A NOSE JOB IF YOU HAVE YOUR BOOBS DONE, O.K.?

POOR OLD GARY. WE COME OUT OF A RESTAURANT AFTER A NICE SPOT OF LUNCH AND SOME IGNORANT GEEZER SHOVES A CAMERA IN FRONT OF HIS FACE.

THESE PEOPLE WILL DO ANYTHING TO GET A PICTURE WON'T THEY?

I KNOW. I'M SURPRISED GARY DIDN'T THUMP THE MAN...

HE CAN'T CAN HE? THE TABLOIDS WOULD RUN THE STORY AND MAKE HIM LOOK SILLY.

I CAN IMAGINE THE HEADLINE NOW.

"JAPANESE TOURISTS FAIL TO RECOGNISE STAR."

WE ALL LOOK THE SAME TO THEM, I SUPPOSE.

JUST PRESS THE RED BUTTON. THANKYOU.

SO YOU'VE DEFINITELY DECIDED TO HAVE YOUR BODY CRYOGENICALLY PRESERVED WHEN YOU FINALLY POP OFF?

YEP.

ONE DAY MEDICAL SCIENCE WILL BRING ME BACK TO LIFE. JUST THINK, I MIGHT STILL BE AROUND IN THE 23RD CENTURY.

ARE YOU SURE YOU KNOW WHAT YOU'RE DOING, GARY?

I MEAN, IT'S A BIG STEP INTO THE UNKNOWN, LET'S FACE IT.

IT DOESN'T FAZE ME IN THE SLIGHTEST, MATE...

I'VE HAD MORE COMEBACKS THAN YOU'VE HAD HOT DINNERS.

..SO ANYWAY ME AND THIS BIRD GET TALKING AND SHE SAYS THAT SHE WANTS TO GET TO KNOW MY BODY - INTIMATELY...

NEXT THING I KNOW SHE'S ALL OVER ME, MATE. HANDS ABSOLUTELY EVERYWHERE.

YOU LUCKY OLD DOG, GARY. YOU'RE IN THERE THEN EH?

MADAME TUSSAUDS, YEAH. ABOUT TIME TOO.

HOW LONG DOES IT TAKE TO MEASURE SOMEONE UP FOR THEIR DUMMY?

RIGHT. I'M OFF TO THE T.V. STUDIO TO DO MY BIT FOR COMIC RELIEF.

GOOD FOR YOU, GARY.

IT'S GOING TO BE A REAL CHARITY MARATHON THIS YEAR. DOESN'T FINISH UNTIL 3 IN THE MORNING.

CRIKEY. YOU'LL BE SHATTERED, MATE.

BEFORE YOU GO: "DON'T FORGET YOUR NOSE."

NO NEED. THERE'LL BE PLENTY THERE AT THE STUDIO FOR US TO USE, I'M SURE.

BETTER TAKE THIS STUPID LITTLE THING TO WEAR THOUGH I SUPPOSE.

WELL I WARNED HIM YEARS AGO ABOUT THE DANGERS OF GETTING TOO INVOLVED IN THE DEMON WHITE POWDER BUT HE WOULDN'T LISTEN...

I MEAN LOTS OF US CELEBRITIES GET TEMPTED. IT'S THE LIFESTYLE ISN'T IT? BUT WHEN YOU'RE OFFERED IT, IF YOU'RE SMART YOU JUST SAY NO.

COULD'VE DESTROYED HIS CAREER, THAT STUFF. YOU KNOW...

I'M JUST GLAD HE'S PULLED HIMSELF TOGETHER AND DECIDED TO PACK IT IN... AS A HIGH PROFILE FIGURE HE WAS BECOMING AN EMBARRASSMENT.

YOU CAN SAY THAT AGAIN...

ABOUT AS STREET CRED AS FAIRY LIQUID.

SHOWBIZ NEWS
DANNY BAKER TO QUIT DAZ COMMERCIALS

7, 15, 22... DAMN..

OH DEAR!

EVERY SUNDAY MORNING HE GOES THROUGH THE SAME SILLY RITUAL TO SEE IF HE'S BEEN LUCKY OR NOT.

BLAST.

IT'S PATHETIC IF YOU ASK ME.

A PERSON OF GARY'S WEALTH CHECKING IF HE'S WON THE NATIONAL LOTTERY?

NO. GARY TOTTING UP THE COLUMN INCHES HE'S GOT IN THE TABLOIDS AND SUPPLEMENTS.

OH WELL. BETTER LUCK NEXT WEEK.

ROD, YOU TARTAN TERROR! YOU ANNOUNCE YOU'RE RETIRING FROM SHOWBIZ ON THE SUNDAY THEN ON THE MONDAY YOU SAY IT WAS ALL A MISTAKE.

I'D HAD A FEW BEVVIES TOO MANY, GARY. I DIDN'T KNOW WHAT I WAS SAYING...

PEOPLE ARE NOW SUGGESTING IT WAS JUST A CHEAP PUBLICITY TRICK TO SELL TICKETS FOR YOUR WORLD TOUR.

NOTHING COULD BE FURTHER FROM THE TRUTH, MATE.

MY PR CHARGED ME A FORTUNE FOR THINKING UP THAT STUNT.

LET'S JUST HOPE IT WORKS, EH?

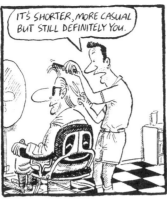

TWO WEEKS AFTER ANNOUNCING HE SUFFERS FROM "PARADISE SYNDROME" - (CELEBRITIES WHO KEEP THINKING THEY'RE SERIOUSLY ILL?)...

GARY BLOKE HAS BEEN RUSHED INTO HOSPITAL WITH A NUMBER OF SERIOUS ILLNESSES...

WHILE FANS HOLD VIGIL OUTSIDE, DOCTORS ARE DESCRIBING HIS CONDITION AS "CRITICAL".

WHAT DO YOU MEAN THERE'S NOTHING WRONG WITH ME?! I DEMAND A 39TH OPINION!

GARY WITH ANOTHER DOCTOR?

YEAH. HE STILL CAN'T ACCEPT IT'S ALL IN HIS HEAD AND HE JUST FEELS ILL TO GET ATTENTION.

EVER COMPLAIN OF PAIN HERE?

YES

AND HERE AND HERE?

YES

SAD ISN'T IT?

AND SO OBVIOUS TO EVERYONE BUT GARY.

THE WORLD

AND HERE?

SEVERAL TIMES.

ALL THESE SYMPTOMS YOU'RE COMPLAINING OF ARE JUST PART OF YOUR PARADISE SYNDROME HYPOCHONDRIA...

YOUR LIFESTYLE IS SO PERFECT, YOU HAVE EVERYTHING YOU WANT, SO YOU IMAGINE THERE'S SOMETHING WRONG TO COMPENSATE.

I'LL CHECK YOUR REFLEXES ANYWAY JUST TO BE ON THE SAFE SIDE.

GENTLE TAP

OWWW! YOU COULD'VE SHATTERED MY KNEE CAP. GET A HELICOPTER AMBULANCE HERE NOW!

SEE?

AFTER MONTHS OF THE FINEST MEDICAL TREATMENT MONEY CAN BUY I NOW ACCEPT THAT I'M JUST A VICTIM OF "PARADISE SYNDROME" WELCOME HOME, GARY.

MY BODY IS PERFECTLY HEALTHY I JUST KEEP THINKING I'M ILL, THAT'S ALL.

SO YOU'RE BACK TO YOUR OLD SELF THEN.

THERE'S NOTHING PHYSICALLY WRONG WITH ME WHATSO-EVER. IT'S ALL IN MY BLOOMIN' HEAD!

SO I'VE MADE APPOINTMENTS WITH THE BEST TEN SHRINKS IN THE WORLD. I LEAVE FOR SYDNEY TOMORROW...

UH-OH.

89

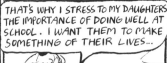

A LETTER FROM YOUR DAUGHTER'S HEADMISTRESS, SIR, ASKING YOU A FAVOUR.

SHE'D LIKE YOU TO JUDGE THE SCHOOL'S HOUSE MUSIC COMPETITION AT THE END OF TERM.

OH BLIMEY.

WHY ASK ME?

YOU'RE A ROCK STAR SIR.

EXACTLY. I DON'T KNOW THE FIRST THING ABOUT HOUSE MUSIC. I'M MORE OF A LYRIC AND MELODY MAN....

EXECUTIVE CAB SERVICE? GOOD EVENING... I REQUIRE AN URGENT CONVEYANCE FOR MR GARY BLOKE...

YES... I'M AFRAID HIS CHAUFFEUR LET HIM DOWN AT THE LAST MINUTE... HE HAS TO BE AT LEICESTER SQUARE IN HALF AN HOUR...

THE PICK-UP ADDRESS FOR THE CAR IS 12, FORTESCUE GARDENS, BELGRAVIA... HOW LONG WILL IT BE, PLEASE?...AH, I'LL TELL HIM...

SEVENTEEN FEET, SIR...

FORGET IT THEN... NO SELF-RESPECTING CELEBRITY TURNS UP AT A PREMIERE IN ANY LIMO UNDER 25 FOOT LONG...

AN OFFICIAL FORM FROM THE STATE OF CALIFORNIA ABOUT INCREASING YOUR ALIMONY PAYMENTS, SIR.

OH NO...

THEY WANT TO ASSESS HOW YOUR CIRCUMSTANCES HAVE CHANGED SINCE THE LAST ARRANGEMENT.

BASTARDS.

WHAT SHALL I PUT DOWN IN THE SECTION HEADED DEPENDENTS?

UM...

PUT "CLEAN. AND HAVE BEEN FOR YEARS."..

SO YOU SPENT THE FESTIVE HOLIDAY SEASON IN ENGLAND THIS TIME? RADICAL, GARY!

YEAH. I THOUGHT SOD BARBADOS AND ALL THAT SUPERFICIAL SHOWBIZ BULLSHIT, LET'S HAVE A SIMPLE FAMILY XMAS AT HOME.

ENJOY IT?

NAH. IT WAS A BIT OF A LETDOWN TO BE HONEST. WE WON'T DO IT AGAIN.

THE KIDS WERE ALL REALLY HOPING FOR A TRADITIONAL WHITE CHRISTMAS BUT UNFORTUNATELY IT WASN'T TO BE...

THE BLOODY ARTIFICIAL SNOW MACHINE PACKED IN.

WHAT A BITCH, MAN.

Also from Masterley Publishing

The Best of Alex 2002
By Charles Peattie & Russell Taylor

The BEST OF ALEX 2002 is the latest installment in the corporate adventures of ALEX the pinstriped cartoon character who appears daily on the business pages of the DAILY TELEGRAPH.

It's been the toughest year so far in Alex's fifteen year career. The financial world is rocked by scandals (Enron, WorldCom) and the unread small print about shares going down as well as up has come into force with a vengeance. Alex's usual concerns about maximising his Christmas bonus go out of the window as he has to fight a rearguard action to ensure that his name is not included on the regular lists of headcount reductions that are sweeping Megabank, the global investment bank where he is employed.

£9.99 (plus p&p)

Cartoon Originals and Prints

The Celeb and Alex cartoon strip originals are all for sale. A strip measures 4x14 inches. If there's a particular one you want, phone or email us some information about it (the date it appeared, what the punch line was etc.) and we'll let you know if we still have it. If the original is not available, or you are too mean to purchase it, we can make a print of it for you. Originals and prints are signed by the creators.

For further details on details on prices and delivery please call 01371 831846.

Originals, prints and books are available from:

Alex
Orchard End,
Watling Lane
Thaxted
CM6 2QY

Tel. 01371 831846
Fax. 01371 831847
Email alex-cartoon@etgate.co.uk

WWW.ALEXCARTOON.COM